LOVE
Study Guide
FOCUSED™

Living Life

to the

Fullest

BOB AND JUDY HUGHES

CROSSROADS PUBLISHING

Love Focused™ Study Guide

Published by Crossroads Publishing
25283 Cabot Road
Suite 117
Laguna Hills, CA 92653

All Scripture quotations, unless otherwise indicated, are taken from the *Holy Bible: New International Version* (NIV). Copyright © 1973, 1978, 1984, by the International Bible Society. Used by permission of Zondervan Publishing House.

Printed in the United States of America.
ISBN 13: 978-0-9800772-1-6
ISBN 10: 0-9800772-1-4

Graphic design by Betty Hopkins

Contents

How to Use This Study Guide

Love Focused will help you discover a very different approach to life and God that makes living in a difficult world simple, satisfying, and successful. It describes a model for living that frees you to enjoy a better life without having to change or control your world. And most importantly, *Love Focused* will help you to succeed at the two things God says are most important: loving God and loving others.

This study is thought-provoking and challenging, but above all, God-centered. Our prayer is that it will greatly impact your life and faith. The following is a brief explanation of how to use each of the different sections in this study.

 READ This is a 14-week group study that follows the fourteen chapters of the book, *Love Focused: Living Life to the Fullest*. It is recommended that you meet on a weekly basis, if possible. The **READ** section gives the reading assignment for the week, which will be one chapter of the book each week.

 RESPOND The **RESPOND** question(s) are designed for your own private reflection, and not for group sharing, unless you choose to do so. You will want to read the **RESPOND** question(s) before beginning your reading for the week, since it will be helpful to have those questions in mind as you read.

 DISCUSS Each week, answer the **DISCUSS** questions prior to coming to your group meeting. These questions are designed for your group to discuss during your meeting time.

Prior to beginning your group discussion each week, give anyone who wishes to do so an opportunity to share thoughts from the **RESPOND** question(s), but only on a voluntary basis. Then, go through the group discussion questions together. Do not feel pressured to answer every single question. These questions are meant to guide your discussion, not control it. It is better to allow meaningful discussion instead of just "getting through all the questions."

 SHARE The **SHARE** time is an "open" discussion time. Take a few minutes during this time to share your thoughts, feelings, challenges, questions, struggles, victories, etc.

 PREPARE Before concluding your group time, read together the **RESPOND** question(s) for the following week, so you will be prepared to record your responses throughout the week.

PART ONE
THE UNSEEN STRUGGLE

Chapter 1

Where Are We Headed?

 READ

Love Focused: Living Life to the Fullest, Chapter One

 RESPOND *(private reflection)*

As we begin this study, pray and ask the Holy Spirit to raise your level of awareness about how Love Focused you are. This week, ask God to show you when you are not Love Focused. Then ask him to help you make his command to love your highest priority and motivation.

List below the areas in which you think God would want you to be more Love Focused.

DISCUSS *(group interaction)*

Give any group member who wishes to do so an opportunity to share thoughts from the **RESPOND** question(s) above.

1. What things do people tend to make more important than God's priority of loving God and loving others?

2. Define the term Love Focused. In what situations are you most likely to be Love Focused?

3. Take some time to consider your own priorities. In what areas of your life has the Great Commandment not been the most important thing? Why do you think that is?

4. What is it about obeying the Great Commandment that makes it difficult?

5. A different approach to explaining behavior is presented in his chapter. How would you explain it? How does it differ with traditional psychology?

What are the "benefits" to this explanation of behavior?

6. In what ways can a person use his or her past experiences as an excuse for present wrong behavior? Have you ever done that? In what ways?

7. Give three examples from your own life of how future goals determined your behavior.

8. Describe a recent time when you got upset or angry. What goal were you pursuing?

9. List some goals that you have pursued that have caused relational problems in your life. For example: "I have to be right," I have to be respected, or "I have to avoid conflict."

SHARE

Was there a particular truth or idea in this week's lesson that was especially helpful? Is there a question you have or a situation in which you would like the group's help in applying these principles?

PREPARE

• Read together the **RESPOND** question(s) for next week, on the following page, so you will be prepared to record your responses throughout the week.

• Before meeting next week, read the assigned chapter, and answer the **RESPOND** and **DISCUSS** questions.

Chapter 2

Now What Do We Do?

READ

Love Focused: Living Life to the Fullest, Chapter Two

RESPOND *(private reflection)*

Consider the following statement from this chapter: "Whether we are aware of it or not, many of our behaviors, thoughts and feelings are connected to unmet emotional needs and the problem of pain." As you go through your week, watch for situations when you do not feel loved, valued or respected.

How did you feel and behave at those times? In addition, watch for situations when you are hurt, or are afraid of getting hurt. How did you feel and behave at those times?

Even though you *felt* unloved and disrespected when the above things happened, did you also come to the conclusion that those feelings were true? If you did use your feelings as a measure of truth, how did that affect your response?

 DISCUSS *(group interaction)*

Give any group member who wishes to do so an opportunity to share thoughts from the **RESPOND** question(s) above.

1. Our secular society tends to explain man's problems by using psychological terms like abandonment, trust issues, intimacy issues etc. Discuss the implications and dangers of explaining man's fundamental problem as being psychological and not spiritual.

2. Which of these two areas of neediness that resulted from the Fall affect your life the most—the need for love and value, or the fear of pain?

3. Read Genesis 3:8–10. How did Adam's fear of pain affect his response to God? How does your fear of pain affect your relationship with God?

4. When are you most likely to be motivated by your fear of getting hurt?

5. Name several problems we face when we look to other people to meet our needs. Give personal examples.

6. Discuss several ways TV and radio advertisers sell products by appealing to our personal needs. Give an example of something you've purchased out of a sense of neediness.

7. Why is it important to distinguish between needs and desires? What happens if we think a desire is a need?

8. What things are you likely to call needs that are really desires? Why do you think you need it?

9. When are you most likely to use feelings or circumstances to measure whether God is meeting your needs?

10. Complete the following statement: I know God meets all my needs because . . .

11. Complete the following statement: Sometimes I don't think God is meeting all my needs because . . .

SHARE

Was there a particular truth or idea in this week's lesson that was especially helpful? Is there a question you have or a situation in which you would like the group's help in applying these principles?

PREPARE

• Read together the **RESPOND** question(s) for next week, on the following page, so you will be prepared to record your responses throughout the week.

• Before meeting next week, read the assigned chapter, and answer the **RESPOND** and **DISCUSS** questions.

PART TWO
IDENTIFYING THE PROBLEM

Chapter 3

What's Your Agenda?

READ

Love Focused: Living Life to the Fullest, Chapter Three

RESPOND *(private reflection)*

In what specific ways has your agenda of getting your emotional needs met and avoiding pain directed and controlled your life:

This past week?

In the past months and years?

DISCUSS *(group interaction)*

Give any group member who wishes to do so an opportunity to share thoughts from the **RESPOND** question(s) above.

1. When we are not trusting God to meet our needs, we go out the door each morning with a personal agenda (plan) to get our emotional needs met and avoid pain. Would you say you've been aware of having a personal agenda? Why or why not?

2. When are you more likely to be tempted to rely on your personal agenda rather than God to get your emotional needs met? For example: At a shopping mall, reading a glamour magazine, at a car show, when a co-worker is promoted, watching a television commercial, watching your child compete in sports, music, drama, academic or other activities, etc.

3. When are you more likely to be tempted to rely on your personal agenda rather than God to avoid emotional pain? For example: At a restaurant, watching TV, reading a romance novel, planning a vacation, surfing the internet, at work, disciplining the kids, etc?

4. Why do you think we naturally look to the world to solve the problem of our emotional needs and pain rather than look to God?

5. Do you think the concept of a personal agenda is universal to all people and cultures? Why or why not?

6. How can our personal agenda affect our lives in negative ways?

7. Read Luke 11:37–43 Why did Jesus rebuke the Pharisees so strongly? What was the Pharisees' personal agenda that motivated their actions?

8. List and discuss some common unhealthy motivations that people have.

9, Regularly asking ourselves why we do what we do helps us see when we are relying on our own plan (agenda) to meet our needs rather than God. When God looks at the motivations behind your behavior, what underlying agenda do you think he sees?

SHARE

Was there a particular truth or idea in this week's lesson that was especially helpful? Is there a question you have or a situation in which you would like the group's help in applying these principles?

PREPARE

• Read together the **RESPOND** question(s) for next week, on the following page, so you will be prepared to record your responses throughout the week.

• Before meeting next week, read the assigned chapter, and answer the **RESPOND** and **DISCUSS** questions.

Chapter 4

Our Instinctive Solution

READ

Love Focused: Living Life to the Fullest, Chapter Four

RESPOND *(private reflection)*

Write out a list of some Outcome Focused Goals you can ask God to help you change to Love Focused Goals this week. For example:

Outcome Focused Goal	**New Love Focused Goal**
To get my children to like me	To be patient with my children
To get a promotion at work	To be the best worker I can be
To change my spouse	To love and accept my spouse
_____	_____
_____	_____
_____	_____

DISCUSS *(group interaction)*

Give any group member who wishes to do so an opportunity to share thoughts from the **RESPOND** question(s) above.

Optional: You may find it helpful to break up into separate men's and women's groups to allow for more personalized discussion of the discussion questions, then come back together for the **SHARE** and **PREPARE** time.

1. Have you noticed that everyone naturally tries to get things to turn out a certain way, usually their way? Why do you think this is? Discuss several common examples. Can you think of any part of the Bible that commands us to make sure things turn out a certain way?

2. What does it mean to be Outcome Focused? What is the purpose of an Outcome Focused Goal?

3. In what areas of your life are you likely to feel pressure to achieve certain outcomes? For example, "I need my children to turn out okay," "I need to be successful," "I need to make sure people are happy with me."

4. List and discuss Outcome Focused Goals you have attempted to achieve. Why were these goals important?

5. How do Outcome Focused Goals prevent us from being Love Focused? Give examples.

6. In Luke 10:38–42, the account of Jesus' visit to Mary and Martha illustrates the difference between Love Focused Goals and Outcome Focused Goals. How did their goals differ, and how did their different goals affect their relationship with Jesus?

7. List several fears that can motivate us to pursue Outcome Focused Goals.

8. List some common fears parents experience. How do these fears affect the parenting goals parents pursue and ultimately the way they raise their children?

9. How does a Love Focused Goal differ from an Outcome Focused Goal?

10. Give some examples of the difference between focusing on the process versus focusing on a particular outcome?

11. What do you think is the relationship between pursuing Outcome Focused Goals and stress?

12. Think of a situation you are dealing with right now. List a few of the Outcome Focused Goals you are pursuing in this situation. What are you trying to accomplish by achieving these goals?

    What would it look like to trust God in this situation?

SHARE

Was there a particular truth or idea in this week's lesson that was especially helpful? Is there a question you have or a situation in which you would like the group's help in applying these principles?

PREPARE

• Read together the **RESPOND** question(s) for next week, on the following page, so you will be prepared to record your responses throughout the week.

• Before meeting next week, read the assigned chapter, and answer the **RESPOND** and **DISCUSS** questions.

Notes . . .

Chapter 5

Strategy 1: Self-Protection

READ

Love Focused: Living Life to the Fullest, Chapter Five

RESPOND *(private reflection)*

This week, notice when you are most likely to be tempted to be self-protective rather than to love. How has your self-protection affected your relationship with God and others?

DISCUSS *(group interaction)*

Give any group member who wishes to do so an opportunity to share thoughts from the **RESPOND** question(s) above.

Optional: You may find it helpful to break up into separate men's and women's groups to allow for more personalized discussion of the discussion questions, then come back together for the **SHARE** and **PREPARE** time.

1. Our strategy is made up of the many different things we do each day to achieve our Outcome Focused Goals. Name the two different categories of strategies. Give examples of both.

2. List several examples of self-protective strategies and the Outcome Focused Goals they might be designed to achieve. For example:

Self-Protective Strategy:	**Outcome-Focused Goal:**
Blaming others	To be respected by others
Avoid conflict	To keep my spouse happy
Defensiveness	To be seen as right
Control	To prevent rejection

3. In what ways do our strategies make us self-centered?

4. List some self-protective strategies you are likely to use.

5. When are you most likely to procrastinate? From what are you trying to protect yourself?

6. How have you seen people's self-protective strategies damage relationships? Consider examples from your own life—your childhood, work, friends, family etc.

7. How can our strategies prevent us from growing spiritually?

8. Have you ever thought of yourself as being addicted to something? After reading the section on addictions in this chapter, how would you answer this question now? What do you think you could be addicted to? Has anyone ever suggested you could be addicted to something?

9. Name several ways parents can use self-protective strategies with their children.

10. In what ways can a parent's self-centered strategies negatively affect their children? Give several examples from your own childhood or from your own parenting experience.

11. If you are a parent, what self-protective strategies do you sometimes use with your children? What Outcome Focused Goal have you been trying to achieve?

12. List the most common situations in which you are tempted to use self-protective strategies to try to get your emotional needs met or avoid pain. If you were to choose to trust God in these situations rather than in your self-protective strategies, how would you respond differently?

13. For a dramatic example of self-protection, read I Samuel 15:1–35. List several ways King Saul was self-protective. What was the ultimate consequence he experienced as king?

 SHARE

Was there a particular truth or idea in this week's lesson that was especially helpful? Is there a question you have or a situation in which you would like the group's help in applying these principles?

 PREPARE

- Read together the **RESPOND** question(s) for next week, on the following page, so you will be prepared to record your responses throughout the week.

- Before meeting next week, read the assigned chapter, and answer the **RESPOND** and **DISCUSS** questions.

Notes . . .

Chapter 6

Strategy 2: Self-Fulfillment

READ

Love Focused: Living Life to the Fullest, Chapter Six

RESPOND *(private reflection)*

This week, notice when you are most likely to be tempted to pursue self-fulfillment rather than to love. How has your strategy of self-fulfillment affected your relationship with God and others?

DISCUSS (group interaction)

Give any group member who wishes to do so an opportunity to share thoughts from the **RESPOND** question(s) above.

Optional: You may find it helpful to break up into separate men's and women's groups to allow for more personalized discussion of the discussion questions, then come back together for the **SHARE** and **PREPARE** time.

1. List several examples of self-fulfillment strategies and the Outcome-Focused Goals they might be designed to achieve. For example:

Self-Fulfillment Strategy:	**Outcome Focused Goal:**
Nagging	To get my husband to change
Bragging	To get people to think I'm smart
Being Critical	To look better than others
_____	_____
_____	_____
_____	_____

2. Which self-fulfillment strategies are you most likely to use?

3. In what ways does our tendency to put too much importance on what others think of us affect how we relate to others?

4. Has the above tendency ever kept you from doing what God wanted you to do? (For example, witnessing to a friend.) Explain.

5. In what ways can being over-committed and too busy be the result of our self-fulfillment strategies?

6. How do you feel when someone gives you an unexpected gift? Do you ever feel uncomfortable or pressured to do something kind in return? Why do you think that is?

   What might that pressure tell us about the goals we are pursuing and where we are looking to meet our needs?

7. Name several ways parents can use self-fulfillment strategies with their children. How have you seen children be negatively affected by parents who use such strategies?

8. If you are a parent, what self-fulfillment strategies do you sometimes use with your children? What Outcome Focused Goals have you been trying to achieve?

9. List the most common situations in which you are tempted to use self-fulfillment strategies to try to get your needs met or avoid pain. If you were to choose to trust God in these situations rather than in your self-fulfillment strategies, how would you respond differently?

10. In the previous lesson, we looked at self-protection in the life of King Saul. (I Samuel 15: 1–35) Now, look at the same passage, and describe how King Saul's life was also negatively affected by self-fulfillment.

SHARE

Was there a particular truth or idea in this week's lesson that was especially helpful? Is there a question you have or a situation in which you would like the group's help in applying these principles?

PREPARE

- Read together the **RESPOND** question(s) for next week, on the following page, so you will be prepared to record your responses throughout the week.

- Before meeting next week, read the assigned chapter, and answer the RESPOND and DISCUSS questions.

Chapter 7

Trying to Make Things Work

READ

Love Focused: Living Life to the Fullest, Chapter Seven

RESPOND *(private reflection)*

Since fear lies beneath control, what fear is likely to cause you to try to control? In what ways do you try to control to protect yourself from pain? For example, "I try to make everyone in my family happy so that no one gets angry with me" or "I try to get my employees to do things perfectly so I'm never criticized."

DISCUSS *(group interaction)*

Give any group member who wishes to do so an opportunity to share thoughts from the **RESPOND** question(s) above.

Optional: You may find it helpful to break up into separate men's and women's groups to allow for more personalized discussion of the discussion questions, then come back together for the **SHARE** and **PREPARE** time.

1. Explain and discuss how the pursuit of an Outcome Focused Goal forces us to try to control people and things.

2. Describe the characteristics of a typical "control freak."

3. What are some subtle and not so subtle ways people try to control?

4. Why do you think it is so hard to accept the reality that we do not have control?

5. Discuss the difference between control and influence. Give examples.

6. What would it look like for you to trust God with your fear and pain the next time you feel the tendency to control?

7. List and discuss the different ways that parents try to control their teenagers. Can you identify what may be the parents' underlying Outcome Focused Goals?

8. List and discuss the different ways that teenagers try to control their parents. Can you identify what may be the teenager's underlying Outcome Focused Goals?

9. How do you feel when someone is trying to control you? What's the message you get from a controller?

10. Who or what are you most likely to try to control and why? You may want to ask your friends or spouse for help, since it can be hard to see on our own. Or, ask yourself, "When do I feel anxious, unhappy, or uncomfortable? Do I trust God with it or try to alleviate my feelings by fixing or controlling things?"

11. What methods of control do you most often use?

12. How does the wrong belief that we have control affect our relationship with God?

SHARE

Was there a particular truth or idea in this week's lesson that was especially helpful? Is there a question you have or a situation in which you would like the group's help in applying these principles?

PREPARE

• Read together the **RESPOND** question(s) for next week, on the following page, so you will be prepared to record your responses throughout the week.

• Before meeting next week, read the assigned chapter, and answer the **RESPOND** and **DISCUSS** questions.

Chapter 8

Your Alarm Is Going Off

READ

Love Focused: Living Life to the Fullest, Chapter Eight

RESPOND *(private reflection)*

Read over the final section in this chapter, "What to Do With Our Warning Lights." As you go through your week, monitor your "warning lights" and practice using them to help you identify how the pursuit of Outcome Focused Goals are preventing you from trusting God and following his command to love. Make notes below of specific examples.

DISCUSS *(group interaction)*

Give any group member who wishes to do so an opportunity to share thoughts from the **RESPOND** question(s) above.

Optional: You may find it helpful to break up into separate men's and women's groups to allow for more personalized discussion of the discussion questions, then come back together for the **SHARE** and **PREPARE** time.

1. In what ways can our spiritual warning system be helpful?

2. Explain what causes unrighteous anger. How does this explanation differ from what you have heard or previously thought causes anger?

3. How does *needing* versus desiring a specific outcome determine our response to the things that happen throughout our day? Apply this principle to a specific situation that you recently experienced. How might this new understanding cause you to respond differently the next time?

4. Review the section in this chapter entitled, "Two Misconceptions about Anger." How can these two explanations change your perspective and response the next time someone hurts you or you have a really bad day?

5. As a warning light, what does controlling fear tell us we are doing? What causes controlling fear?

6. In what ways and situations do you allow fear to control you? What Outcome Focused Goals lie underneath your controlling fear?

7. What is worry? What is the connection between controlling fear, Outcome Focused Goals, and worry?

8. Why is worrying so attractive?

9. How would you explain why a "worry wart" worries so much?

10. What things are you most likely to worry about and why? What Outcome Focused Goals are behind your worry?

Why does it seem easier to pursue Outcome Focused Goals and to worry than to trust God?

11. Can you identify any compulsive behaviors or activities that you do that are the result of your controlling fear?

12. As a warning light, what does impatience tell us?

13. When are you most likely to struggle with impatience? What Outcome Focused Goals are most often behind your impatience?

14. Several other warning lights are listed in the book. Which ones can you relate to and why?

SHARE

Was there a particular truth or idea in this week's lesson that was especially helpful? Is there a question you have or a situation in which you would like the group's help in applying these principles?

PREPARE

- Read together the **RESPOND** question(s) for next week, on the following page, so you will be prepared to record your responses throughout the week.

- Before meeting next week, read the assigned chapter, and answer the **RESPOND** and **DISCUSS** questions.

PART THREE
THE POWER TO LOVE

Chapter 9

God's Solution

READ

Love Focused: Living Life to the Fullest, Chapter Nine

RESPOND *(private reflection)*

This week, in what new areas of your life could you choose to believe that God is enough? As you choose to believe that God is enough and is in control of the outcome, look for new opportunities and new ways you can love God and others. Record your thoughts and experiences below.

 DISCUSS *(group interaction)*

Give any group member who wishes to do so an opportunity to share thoughts from the **RESPOND** question(s) above.

1. When Adam and Eve were in the paradise of the Garden of Eden, they still sinned. How would you explain why they still sinned?

2. In what ways can we be tempted in the same ways as Adam and Eve were?

3. The disciples personally experienced Jesus' love twenty-four hours a day for three years, yet they still chose to pursue their own agenda over God's plan. They selfishly argued about who would be the greatest in heaven, Peter denied Christ three times, Thomas doubted the resurrection, and Judas betrayed Jesus. What does their behavior in the midst of Jesus' perfect love tell you about what they believed? Why was their self-fulfilling and self-protective behavior a sin? (See Hebrews 11:6 and Romans 14:23).

4. How would you describe the difference between knowing God loves you and believing that God's love and grace is also enough?

5. Discuss the significance of 2 Corinthians 9:8, 2 Peter 1:3, Philippians 4:19, and 2 Corinthians 12:9 in terms of God's provision for us.

6. Why do you think it can be difficult to choose to believe God's love and grace are enough?

7. What are you likely to fill in the blank in the equation: God's love and grace plus _____ equals my needs are satisfied?

8. In what areas of your life are you trusting that God is enough?

9. In what areas of your life do you find it difficult to trust that God is enough? Why?

10. Which of the two-gasoline tanker truck drivers can you relate to and why?

11. Explain why Paul was able to be content in prison (Philippians 4:11–13).

12. In what areas of your life are you not content? What can you learn from Paul and from this lesson that will help you to be more content?

SHARE

Was there a particular truth or idea in this week's lesson that was especially helpful? Is there a question you have or a situation in which you would like the group's help in applying these principles?

PREPARE

• Read together the **RESPOND** question(s) for next week, on the following page, so you will be prepared to record your responses throughout the week.

• Before meeting next week, read the assigned chapter, and answer the **RESPOND** and **DISCUSS** questions.

Chapter 10

A Closer Look

READ

Love Focused: Living Life to the Fullest, Chapter Ten

RESPOND *(private reflection)*

Are there some things in your life that you are mistakenly calling "needs" that should really just be desires? If so, list them here, and ask God to help you see them as desires.

DISCUSS *(group interaction)*

Give any group member who wishes to do so an opportunity to share thoughts from the **RESPOND** question(s) above.

1. In what ways can believing that God is enough improve our relationships?

2. Which of the inaccurate ways to measure whether God is good discussed in this chapter are you most likely to use? Are there any others that you use?

3. The presence of unhealthy behavior and negative emotions like anger, depression and frustration is often an indicator that we have not completely given up the belief that the world can fully satisfy us. Based on these indicators, would you say you have completely accepted this truth? Why or why not? If not, list those areas where you are still trying to get someone or something to come through for you.

4. In what situations are you likely to use emotions and circumstances to measure whether God's love and grace are enough? How have you done so recently?

5. Are you aware of being afraid of trusting God in certain areas of your life? Why?

   How would your life be different if you were to live more by your beliefs rather than by your emotions?

6. In what ways do you think people most often confuse desires with needs?

7. What are some things that might indicate that someone is confusing desires with needs?

8. Refer to your answer in the **RESPOND** question above. What Outcome Focused Goals are you pursuing in response to the things that you have been calling "needs"? (i.e., I need to be successful so I have to "make sure everyone likes me and thinks I'm smart.")

9. In *The Case for Faith* (Zondervan, 2000), Lee Strobel says, "Ultimately, though, faith isn't about having perfect and complete answers . . . After all, we don't demand that level of conclusive proof in any other area of life." Discuss this statement in light of the "choice to believe God is enough." How does this idea change your perspective on how to grow in your faith?

10. Think back to before you began this study. In general, are you less Outcome Focused or about the same? If you answered less, how has that change affected your emotions, behaviors and relationships? Give specific examples.

11. What concepts and truths discussed in this chapter or others do you think are most important to being able to be less Outcome Focused and more Love Focused?

12. When we step out in faith, and choose to believe God is enough in spite of the circumstances and how we feel, we're "betting the farm on God." List the area(s) where you need to take this step of faith. What would it practically look like to "bet the farm on God" in these situations?

SHARE

Was there a particular truth or idea in this week's lesson that was especially helpful? Is there a question you have or a situation in which you would like the group's help in applying these principles?

PREPARE

• Read together the **RESPOND** question(s) for next week, on the following page, so you will be prepared to record your responses throughout the week.

• Before meeting next week, read the assigned chapter, and answer the **RESPOND** and **DISCUSS** questions.

PART FOUR
APPLICATION

Chapter 11

When Pleasing God Isn't So Pleasing

READ

Love Focused: Living Life to the Fullest, Chapter Eleven

RESPOND *(private reflection)*

Legalism is an attempt to control God. In light of that perspective, consider the motivations behind the things you do—working, serving, being kind, reading your Bible etc. Are there things that you do that are partly designed to get God to do what you want?

What do your attempts to control God tell you about your beliefs about God, and about how he relates to his children?

DISCUSS *(group interaction)*

Give any group member who wishes to do so an opportunity to share thoughts from the **RESPOND** question(s) above.

1. How would you define legalism?

2. What do you think are the most common ways people are legalistic? How would you explain why it is so natural for a person to be legalistic?

3. Ephesians 2:8–9 says, "For it is by grace you have been saved, through faith . . . " How would you explain what this verse means and how it practically applies to a Christian's life?

4. According to James 2:10, if a person tries to please God by keeping the law, what happens if he commits one sin? What are the practical implications of this verse?

5. Religious Legalism is man's attempt to please God for the wrong reasons. List the areas in your life where you are possibly trying to do "good works" to earn God's love, acceptance and blessing.

6. Consider the following statement from this chapter: "We mistakenly believe that God deals with us differently after the point of salvation." Read Galatians 3:3 and Colossians 2:6.

In what areas of your life do you feel pressure to live a "good" life? Where do you think this pressure is coming from?

7. This chapter takes a "different look at legalism." How do the authors define legalism?

8. What is at the very core of legalism, the fundamental reason we pursue it?

   In light of this, complete the following statement:

   "I pursue legalism in the area(s) of _____ because I

   _____ .

9. How would you define grace?

10. What is the motivation of grace, and how does it differ from the motivation of legalism?

List some of the specific differences between legalism and grace.

11. Why did Christ rebuke the pharisees so strongly? What were they doing wrong? In what ways can people act like pharisees today? (*See* Luke 16:15, 11:39, and Matthew 23:5)

12. Why do you think it can be so hard to accept God's free gift of grace?

As you continue to serve God and others this week, thank him that his love and acceptance of you is independent of your performance. Then, enjoy doing your "good works" knowing that God deals with you exactly the same after salvation as before, based on his grace, never your performance.

SHARE

Was there a particular truth or idea in this week's lesson that was especially helpful? Is there a question you have or a situation in which you would like the group's help in applying these principles?

PREPARE

- Read together the **RESPOND** question(s) for next week, on the following page, so you will be prepared to record your responses throughout the week.

- Before meeting next week, read the assigned chapter, and answer the **RESPOND** and **DISCUSS** questions.

Chapter 12

Just Do It Right

READ

Love Focused: Living Life to the Fullest, Chapter Twelve

RESPOND *(private reflection)*

Whether you are a perfectionist in every area of your life or just in a few areas, pursuing perfection is not God's best for you or others. With God's help this week, look for opportunities to trust God to be enough for you as you choose to stop short of doing something "perfectly" or in the case of interpersonal perfectionists, requiring *someone* else to live according to your standards. If you feel anxious or uncomfortable (which you probably will), do not use your feelings to measure whether you are doing the right or wrong thing. Choose to do the right thing and trust God for the outcome. Keep a journal of each situation and share your experience with your group.

DISCUSS *(group interaction)*

Give any group member who wishes to do so an opportunity to share thoughts from the **RESPOND** question(s) above.

1. Why do you think perfectionism is so common?

2. What are the two purposes of perfectionism?

3. What are some common fears that can motivate perfectionism?

4. According to the authors, "The legalist uses his performance to please God. The perfectionist tries to be perfect to win the approval of other people." In what ways have you seen people try to use perfectionism to win approval?

5. Have you ever been negatively affected by someone else's perfectionism? How did it affect you emotionally and relationally?

6. Why do you think perfectionists so often deny their perfectionism is a problem?

7. The authors sate that, "A perfectionist is driven, a healthy person has drive." How would you explain to your child, or to a friend, how to achieve in life without pursuing perfectionism?

8. This chapter lists several statements commonly made by perfectionists. Which one(s) can you relate to and why?

9. This chapter lists four different types of perfectionists. Before answering question eight, and reading these four descriptions, would you have identified yourself as a perfectionist? Would you now? If yes, which of the four types of perfectionists most closely describes you?

10. Do you think you are more likely to try to perfect yourself or other people? (Ask your family and friends!) Complete the following statements:

    If I don't do _____ well enough, then

    _____ .

    If I can't get _____ to do things the way I think is right, then _____ .

    What are the fears that are driving your perfectionism?

11. If you have identified yourself as one or more of the types of perfectionists, how has your perfectionism affected your life—emotionally, relationally, spiritually? How have others told you it affects them? How has it kept you from loving them?

12. How might trusting that God is enough rather than trusting in your perfectionism specifically change your behavior in the days ahead at work, at home, with family and friends?

SHARE

Was there a particular truth or idea in this week's lesson that was especially helpful? Is there a question you have or a situation in which you would like the group's help in applying these principles?

PREPARE

- Read together the **RESPOND** question(s) for next week, on the following page, so you will be prepared to record your responses throughout the week.

- Before meeting next week, read the assigned chapter, and answer the **RESPOND** and **DISCUSS** questions.

Chapter 13

Putting It All Together

READ

Love Focused: Living Life to the Fullest, Chapter Thirteen

RESPOND *(private reflection)*

This week, pay close attention to your spiritual warning system. What is it telling you? How have your thoughts, emotions, words and actions demonstrated that you did or *did not* believe that God is enough?

DISCUSS *(group interaction)*

Give any group member who wishes to do so an opportunity to share thoughts from the **RESPOND** question(s) above.

1. Why is it that common formulas for spiritual growth which focus primarily on just "doing something different" are usually not that effective long term? How have you personally experienced this to be true?

2. Think about how you *typically* respond when things don't go the way you want. Based on your response, do you think you have fully accepted the reality that the world will never fully satisfy? Why or why not?

3. Do you think you have fully accepted the reality that you do not have control? Why or why not? If not, why do you think you are hesitating to do so?

   If not, in what ways are you still holding on to that false belief?

   For example, "IF I raise my children the right way, THEN they'll turn out okay." Or, "IF I work hard, THEN I can guarantee success." OR,

   IF _____ THEN _____

   IF _____ THEN _____

   IF _____ THEN _____

   IF _____ THEN _____

   IF _____ THEN _____

4. How has attempting to control certain areas of your life affected you emotionally, spiritually, and physically? How has it affected your relationships with friends, family and God?

5. What would you say are the biggest benefits to accepting the reality that you do *not* have control?

6. Why is it so important to submit our wills to the Holy Spirit? What does it practically mean to present ourselves as a living sacrifice? (Romans 12:1) Give specific examples.

7. How does the safety net of believing that God's love and grace is enough help in the process of surrendering our wills to God's?

8. What does it mean to let go of our agenda? Why can it be so hard to do?

9. Can you think of a time when you switched strategies without switching your agenda— perhaps as a young child or teenager, and now as an adult?

10. What is required in order for us to let go of our Outcome Focused Goals and strategies? Why do you think it can be so difficult?

11. How would you describe the process of putting more of your faith in God? How does "thanking God" practically help us to trust God more?

12. In simple terms, growing in Christ means we learn to "Love God, love others, and trust God for the outcome." In what specific areas of your life do you need to focus more on the process of loving others and trusting God for the outcomes? What will this look like on a daily basis?

As you choose to make the changes you gave above, how do you think your life will change?

Case Study (optional)

As a group, discuss the following fictitious case study and list the possible Outcome Focused Goals, strategies, warning lights, compulsions, wrong beliefs, etc. What do you think would help this couple to be more Love Focused?

Tom is forty years old and has been married to Mary for fifteen years. They have two sons, twelve and ten. Tom is the vice-president of his company and is a workaholic. For the past several years, he has been having an affair with his secretary. Tom is known as a nice guy and a good provider for his family. However, he is not a good spiritual leader—he says he leaves that up to Mary. Tom watches sports on TV all weekend and rarely does any work around the house. He often gets angry at Mary when she is unhappy or upset about something. He says, "She makes me mad when she is not in a good mood."

Mary is very busy, and admits that she is "probably over committed." Each week she teaches one women's Bible study and attends a second one. She is also the president of the PTA and the team mom for both sons' soccer teams. She admits she is obsessed with romance novels and reality shows on TV. Mary is a worrier who "has to have her children behave well and her home look perfect."

SHARE

Was there a particular truth or idea in this week's lesson that was especially helpful? Is there a question you have or a situation in which you would like the group's help in applying these principles?

PREPARE

- Read together the **RESPOND** question(s) for next week, on the following page, so you will be prepared to record your responses throughout the week.

- Before meeting next week, read the assigned chapter, and answer the **RESPOND** and **DISCUSS** questions.

Chapter 14

Winning at Love

READ

Love Focused: Living Life to the Fullest, Chapter Fourteen

RESPOND *(private reflection)*

In what practical ways can you make being Love Focused a higher priority this next week? Give several examples. In what ways will it require you to trust God more?

DISCUSS *(group interaction)*

Give any group member who wishes to do so an opportunity to share thoughts from the **RESPOND** question(s) above.

1. The questions we ask ourselves reveal our goals. What are some common questions you ask yourself as you go through a typical day? Based on the types of questions you tend to ask most, are the majority of your goals Love Focused or Outcome Focused?

2. Looking back before you began this study, how have the questions you ask yourself changed?

3. What questions are you still sometimes asking yourself that might reveal areas where you are still pursuing Outcome Focused Goals?

4. Doing things safely, comfortably or perfectly are often conditions we require before we do something. Which of these requirements are you likely to add to things you do?

5. How do you typically measure whether you've done the right or wrong thing? By how others respond? How you feel? The outcome? What is the danger in using these yardsticks to measure what we do? What is a better way to measure what you do?

6. When you measure what you do by God's yardstick, how does that change things, perhaps in a specific situation you are dealing with right now?

7. Do you see yourself as an encourager? Do you think others experience you as encouraging? In what ways could you use your speech to more deeply encourage others? Give examples.

8. Why do you think it can be so hard to just listen to another person? When you find yourself "needing" to say something, why do you think that is? In other words, in what ways can saying what we need to say seem more important than simply loving the other person by listening to them?

9. Would you describe yourself more as a talker or a listener? In what situations could you be more Love Focused by listening better?

10. Asking questions can be a powerful way to communicate love. Do you see yourself as a person who uses sincere questions to communicate your love for others? Give examples of questions that others have asked that have encouraged you.

11. Do you think people have to be healed from all their past wounds before they can love others and be used by God? Why or why not? How can others in this group help you to become more Love Focused even though you have experienced deep hurts in your life?

12. Having concluded this study, how have your priorities been reordered? What things have you moved "down" on your "To Do" list, in order to make loving God and loving others a priority?

13. How have you and your relationship with God and others changed as a result of this study? In what ways are you more Love Focused?

    As you continue to trust God to be enough, what areas in your life do you think God wants to help you continue to change?

Case Study (optional)

As a group discuss the following fictitious case study and list the possible Outcome Focused Goals, strategies, warning lights, compulsions, wrong beliefs, etc. What do you think would help this woman be more Love Focused?

Monica is forty-six years old and owns her own real estate business. She has been divorced twice, and has one son. She was molested by an uncle when she was five-years old. Promiscuous in junior high and high school, she got pregnant when she was eighteen. Monica has been an alcoholic for twenty years. She is a new Christian who struggles with growing spiritually because she feels distant from God.

Monica acknowledges she "needs to be in control" of her relationships and works extra hard to help people in need, and to do a good job for her clients. As a result, she is frequently exhausted and often moody if she thinks a client is not pleased with her work.

SHARE

Was there a particular truth or idea in this week's lesson that was especially helpful? Is there a question you have or a situation in which you would like the group's help in applying these principles?

To order additional copies of
Love Focused™ or the *Love Focused*™ *Study Guide*
call
800•301•9891
or go to
www.lovefocused.com

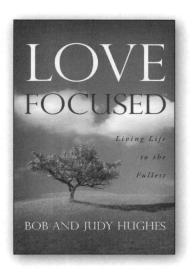
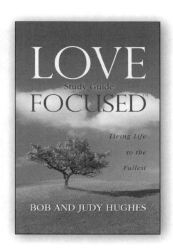

If you would like to receive personal coaching to apply the *Love Focused* Model in specific areas of your life, e-mail **Love Focused Ministries** or go to our website to learn about our Telephone Coaching Program.

LOVE FOCUSED™
Ministries
info@lovefocused.com